Macmillan English
Practice Book

1

Mary Bowen

Printha Ellis

Louis Fidge

Liz Hocking

Wendy Wren

MACMILLAN

Review

1 **Write the letters.**

1 b ___ d

_ a l l

2 c ___ e

_ a t

3 m ___ n

_ u t

4 p ___ q

_ u e e n

5 j ___ y

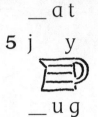

_ u g

6 w ___ v

_ a n

2 **Read and colour.**

1

a red cat

2

a blue bird

3

an orange frog

4

a yellow kite

5

a green ball

6

a purple hat

3 **How many? Write the number.**

1

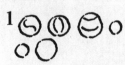

___six___

2

_____

3

_____

4

_____

5

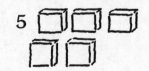

_____

6

_____

4 Look and write.

1 It is a _____.   2 They are _____.

3 It is a _____.   4 They are _____.

5 It is a _____.   6 They are _____.

5 Read and circle.

1   The elephant is   big   little.

2   The mouse is   big   little.

3   The frog is   big   little.

4   The plane is   big   little.

5   The apple is   big   little.

6 Read and colour the right word.

1   The pen is   in   on   the desk.

2   The book is   on   under   the chair.

3   The ruler is   in   on   the bag.

4   The pencil is   in   under   the book.

Unit 1

Reading and understanding

1 **Read and write.**

Ben is six.

Ben's big brother is ten.

Ben's sister is funny.

Ben's baby brother is little.

1 ___Ben___ is six.

2 Ben's _____ _____ is ten.

3 Ben's _____ is funny.

4 Ben's _____ _____ is little.

2 **Read and write.**

Ben's mother is helpful.

Ben's father is tall.

Ben's grandfather and grandmother are kind.

1 Who is tall?

Ben's _____ is tall.

2 Who is helpful?

Ben's _____ is helpful.

3 Who is kind?

Ben's _____ and _____ are kind.

Sentence building

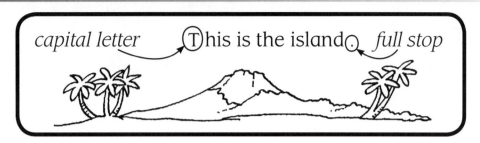

capital letter (T)his is the island(.) *full stop*

1 Circle the capital letters. Circle the full stops.

1   T his is my big brother .

2   H ere is my friend .

3   I am seven .

4   T his is my dad .

5   M y sister is six .

2 Write the sentences correctly.

Remember capital letters and full stops.

1   the boy has a dog
    <u>The boy has a dog.</u>

2   he is nine

   _____

3   my brother is three

   _____

4   she is my friend

   _____

5   this is my mum and dad

   _____

Grammar

1 **Read and match.**

one   (four)   three   seven   six

4   8   1   2   3   10   6   5   7   9

eight   two   ten   five   nine

2 **Look and write.**

1 Look at Freddy.   He is __three__ .

2 Look at Lily.   She _____ .

3 Look at Tom.   _____ .

4 Look at Jane.   _____ .

5 Look at Dan.   _____ .

6 Look at Mike.   _____ .

7 Look at Molly.   _____ .

8 Look at Bill.   _____ .

3 **Draw and write. Like this:**

I am Dan.

I am six.

I am a boy.

This is me. _____

_____

_____

Phonics

1 Say the sounds.
Make the words.

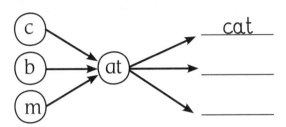

2 Match and write.

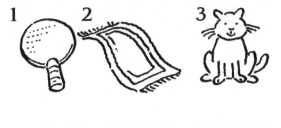

3 Say the sounds. Make the words.

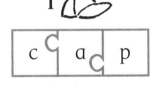 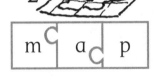 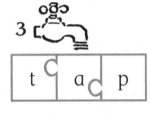

_____   _____   _____

4 Write.

1 The _____ has a _____ .

2 The _____ has a _____ .

3 The _____ and the _____ are on the _____ .

4 The _____ and the _____ are on the _____ .

5 Read and colour.
Colour the *at* words **red**.   Colour the *ap* words **green**.

cat   mat   tap   map   hat

Writing

Write about my friends.

five   six   seven   eight   nine   ten

1 This is Emma. She is nine.

2 This is _____ He is _____ .

3 _____

4 _____

5 _____

6 _____

Your writing

Draw and write about you.

My name is _____ .

I am _____ .

Now draw and write about your friend.

_____

_____

Unit 2

Reading and understanding

1 **Look and read.**

This is Amy's new bedroom.

2 **Choose the words from the box.**

> Yes, it is. No, it isn't.
> Yes, they are. No, they aren't.

1 This is Amy's bed.

_____ .

2 This is Amy's radio.

_____ .

3 This is Amy's desk.

_____ .

4 These are Amy's chairs.

_____ .

5 These are Amy's elephants.

_____ .

6 These are Amy's books.

_____ .

Sentence building

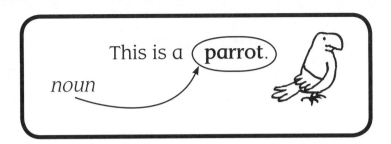

This is a (parrot.)

noun

1 **Find the noun. Circle the noun.**

1 This is my plane.   2 Here is the house.

3 This is a bed.   4 The boy is nine.

5 Here is my mum.   6 This is my radio.

2 **Finish the sentences. Use the nouns in the box.**

chair	ball	book	tree	doll	box

1 This is a _____ .   2 This is a _____ .

3 This is a _____ .   4 This is a _____ .

5 This is a _____ .   6 This is a _____ .

Grammar

1 **Read and match. Write the letter.**

1 This is an elephant. [c]

2 This is a doll. [ ]

3 These are trains. [ ]

4 These are cars. [ ]

5 This is a parrot. [ ]

a

b

c

d

e

2 **Write _This is_ or _These are_.**

1 _____ chairs.

2 _____ a computer.

3 _____ a lamp.

4 _____ tables.

3 **Write the sentences.**

| a toy | a ball | a desk | toys | balls | desks |
| a bed | a plane | a book | beds | planes | books |

1 This is _____ .

2 These are _____ .

3 _____ .

4 _____ .

5 _____ .

6 _____ .

Phonics

1 Say the sounds. Make the words.

| h | e | n | | m | e | n | | t | e | n | | p | e | n |

_____   _____   _____   _____

2 Write.

_____   _____   _____   _____

3 Write.

1   a _____ with a _____

2   _____ _____

3   _____ _____ with a _____

4 Say the sounds.
Make the words.

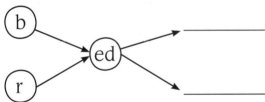

b _____

r _____

ed

_____

_____

5 Colour the bed red.

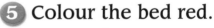

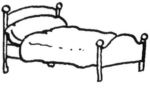

6 Read and match. Write the letter.

1   The hen is on the bed.   ☐   a   [chicken on pen]

2   The pen is on the hen.   ☐   b   [pen on chicken]

3   The hen is on the pen.   ☐   c   [chicken on bed]

13

Writing

Choose a word from the box. Then write.

bed   desk   chairs   computer   books   toys

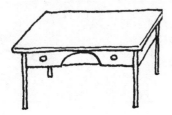

1 This is my _____ .

2 These are my _____ .

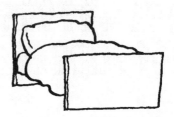

3 _____

_____

4 _____

_____

5 _____

_____

6 _____

_____

Your writing

This is my room.

① Read and colour.

Colour the bed blue.   Colour the books green.

Colour the computer pink.   Colour the desk brown.

Colour the toys red.   Colour the chairs yellow.

② Write about Dan's room.

This is my bed. It is <u>blue.</u> .

This is my desk . It is _____ .

This is my computer. It is _____ .

These are my books . They are _____ .

These are my chairs. They are _____ .

Unit 3

Reading and understanding

1 Look at the picture. Write ✔ or ✗.

1 I can see the moon. ☐ 2 I can see a star. ☐

3 I can see a book. ☐ 4 I can see the sea. ☐

5 I can see a tree. ☐ 6 I can see a chair. ☐

7 I can see a bed. ☐ 8 I can see an owl. ☐

9 I can see a mouse. ☐ 10 I can see a dog. ☐

11 I can see a table. ☐ 12 I can see a cat. ☐

2 Write ✔ or ✗.

1 A star can see. ☐ 2 A star can hear. ☐

3 An owl can see. ☐ 4 An owl can hear. ☐

5 A tree can see. ☐ 6 A tree can hear. ☐

7 A cat can see. ☐ 8 A cat can hear. ☐

Sentence building

> **an** *for words beginning with*   a   e   i   o   u
>
> **a**   *for all other words*

1 Write *a* or *an* for these animals.

 1   This is __an__ ant.

 2   This is _____ cat.

 3   This is _____ elephant.

4   This is _____ dog.

 5   This is _____ owl.

 6   This is _____ fish.

7   This is _____ octopus.

 8   This is _____ snake.

2 Read and circle the correct one.

1   a   orange bird   an   orange bird

2   a   red snake   an   red snake

3   a   old elephant   an   old elephant

4   a   purple flower   an   purple flower

Grammar

1 Read and circle.

1. Can you see a plane? Yes, I can. No, I can't.
2. Can you see the moon? Yes, I can. No, I can't.
3. Can you see a bird? Yes, I can. No, I can't.
4. Can you see a doll? Yes, I can. No, I can't.
5. Can you see the sun? Yes, I can. No, I can't.

2 Look and write *I can see* or *I can't see*.

1 _____ the sun.
2 _____ the moon.
3 _____ a tree.
4 _____ a car.
5 _____ a house.

3 Look and write.

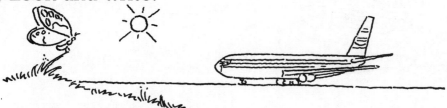

1 I can see the sun.   .
2 I can't _____ moon .
3 I _____ a car .
4 _____ a plane .
5 _____ an elephant .

Phonics

1 Say the sounds.
Make the words.

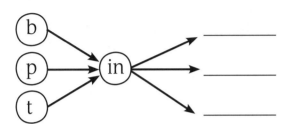

2 Match and write.

_____

_____

_____ _____ _____ _____

3 Circle the words.

q w x t i n r t y   z b i n x c v b n   l k p i n j h g f

4 Write.

1 The _____ is in the _____ .

2 The _____ is in the _____ .

3 The _____ is in the _____ .

5 Choose and write.

big dig    wig dig   big wig

_____   _____   _____

6 Read and colour.

Colour the **in** words pink. Colour the **ig** words green.

(wig)(bin)(pin)(dig)(big)(tin)

Writing

Join the dots. Write.

a bird   the moon   a cat   a tree   a star   a dog

1

_____

2

_____

3

_____

4

_____

5

_____

6

_____

Your writing

Look and write.

I can see the moon.

I can _____ the stars.

I _____ a tree.

_____ a bird.

_____

_____

Check-up 1

Grammar

1 Write *am*, *is* or *are*.

1 Mobi _____ a mobile phone.

2 How old _____ you? I _____ seven.

3 Miss Plum _____ a teacher.

2 Write *This is* or *These are*.

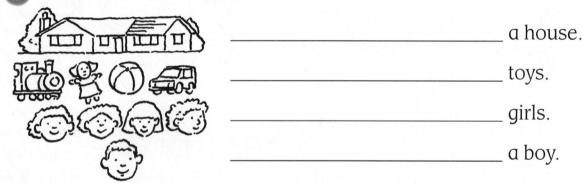

_____ a house.

_____ toys.

_____ girls.

_____ a boy.

3 Write *can* or *can't*.

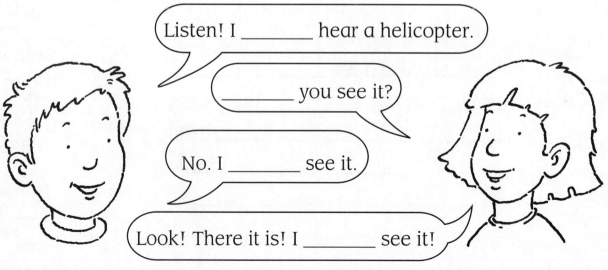

Listen! I _____ hear a helicopter.

_____ you see it?

No. I _____ see it.

Look! There it is! I _____ see it!

Sentence Building

1 Write the sentences with capital letters and full stops.

   1 nina is my friend   _____

   2 she is seven   _____

   3 this is Ben's brother   _____

2 Underline the nouns.

   1 This is my computer.

   2 These are my books.

   3 The boy is six.

3 Write *a* or *an*.

  1   2   3   4   5

_____ dog _____ ant _____ mouse _____ owl _____ snake

Phonics

Choose the correct word.

  bit bat   pen pan   ban bin

_____   _____   _____

Move on with Mobi

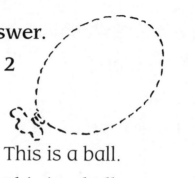

1 Draw. Tick ✔ the correct answer.

1

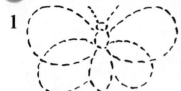

This is a bird. ☐

This is a butterfly. ☐

2

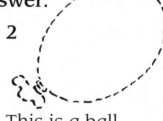

This is a ball. ☐

This is a balloon. ☐

3

This is a house. ☐

This is a mouse. ☐

4

This is a plane. ☐

This is a train. ☐

5

This is the sun. ☐

This is a star. ☐

6

This is a doll. ☐

This is a dog. ☐

7

This is a cat. ☐

This is a hat. ☐

8

This is an egg. ☐

This is an elephant. ☐

Sentence building

1 Circle the capital letters. Circle the question mark.

1 W hat can you see?

2 C an you see the snake?

3 W hat is your name?

4 H ow old are you?

5 A re these your toys?

2 Write some question marks.

? _____ _____ _____

3 Write these questions correctly.

Remember capital letters and question marks.

1 is this your house

_____

2 is this an elephant

_____

3 can you see the frog

_____

Grammar

1 **Write *this* or *these*.**

1 What is _____ ?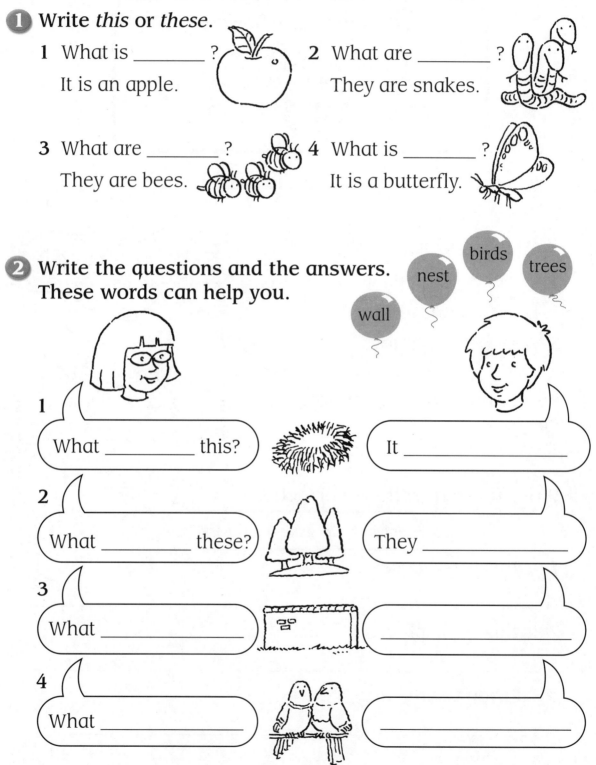
It is an apple.

2 What are _____ ?
They are snakes.

3 What are _____ ?
They are bees.

4 What is _____ ?
It is a butterfly.

2 **Write the questions and the answers.
These words can help you.**

birds   trees

nest

wall

1

What _____ this?

It _____

2

What _____ these?

They _____

3

What _____

_____

4

What _____

_____

28

Phonics

1 Say the sounds. Write the words.

1

b	un

_____

2

r	un

_____

3

s	un

_____

2 Read and match.

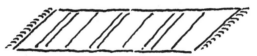 jug rug mug

3 Write.

1

Mum has got a

_____

2

Mum has got a

_____

3

Mum has got a

_____

4

Mum is on a

_____

5

Mum likes the

_____

6

Mum can

_____

Writing

Draw and write.

fish   flower   butterfly   eggs   apples   snakes

1

2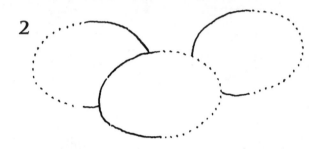

This is a _____

These are _____

3

4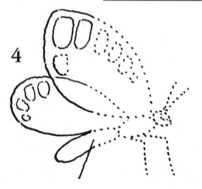

_____

_____

5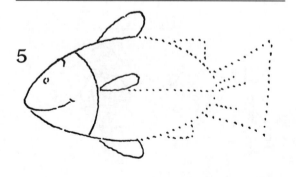

6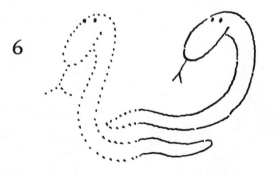

_____

_____

Your writing

Draw and write.

1 Draw two snakes.

What are these?

They are _____

2 Draw a flower.

What is this?

It is a _____

3 Draw a fish.

What is this?

_____

4 Draw three eggs.

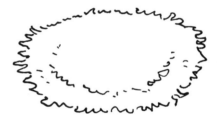

What are these?

_____

5 Draw five apples.

What are these?

_____

6 Draw a butterfly.

What is this?

_____

Unit 5

Reading and understanding

1 Write.

1 This boy is next to Scott.

_____Ben_____ is next to Scott.

2 This boy is next to the table.

_____ is next to the table.

3 This girl is on the chair.

_____ is on the chair.

4 This girl is next to the toy box.

_____ is next to the toy box.

5 This girl is under the table.

_____ is under the table.

6 This boy is between Scott and Sam.

_____ is between Scott and Sam.

Sentence building

> **Adjectives** *tell us more about nouns.*
>
> the ball   the **red** ball

1 **Colour the pictures. Write the adjectives.**

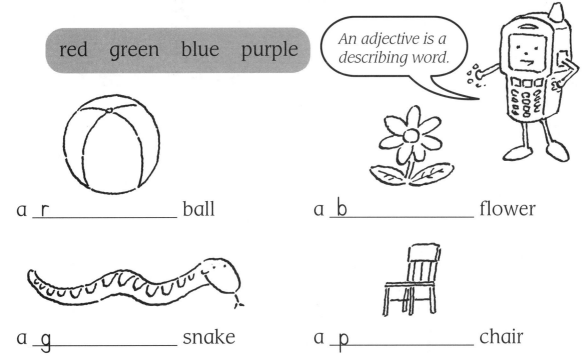

red   green   blue   purple

An adjective is a describing word.

a r_____ ball

a b_____ flower

a g_____ snake

a p_____ chair

2 **Finish the sentences with a colour adjective.**

yellow   grey   blue   green

1 The sea is _____

2 The grass is _____

3 The sun is _____

4 The elephant is _____

Grammar

1 Read and match. Write the letter.

1 on ☐
2 in ☐
3 under ☐
4 next to ☐
5 between ☐

2 Look and write.

1 The pen is _____ the desk.
2 The book is _____ the table.
3 The ruler is _____ the chair.
4 The pencil is _____ the books.

3 Where is the bird? Write.

1   It is _____ the tree.

2   _____

3   _____

4   _____

5   _____

34

Phonics

1 Say the sounds. Write the words.

 d og

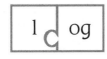 l og

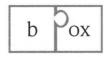 b ox

 f ox

_____   _____   _____   _____

2 Write *yes* or *no*.

1 Is this a dog? _____

2 Is this a log? _____

3 Is this a box? _____

4 Is this a fox? _____

3 Write.

1

The _____ is on a _____ .

2

The _____ is in the _____ .

3

The _____ is in the _____ .

4

The _____ is on the _____ .

4 Match the rhyming words.

dog   box

fox   not

hot   log

5 Write the rhyming words.

_____ and _____

_____ and _____

_____ and _____

Writing

Where is Mobi? Write.

in   on   under   next to   between

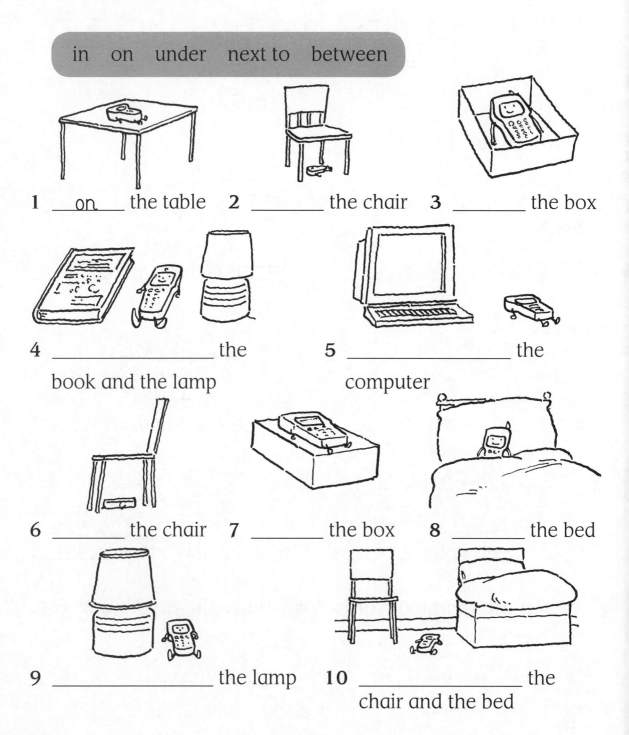

1 __on__ the table   2 _____ the chair   3 _____ the box

4 _____ the
book and the lamp

5 _____ the
computer

6 _____ the chair   7 _____ the box   8 _____ the bed

9 _____ the lamp   10 _____ the
chair and the bed

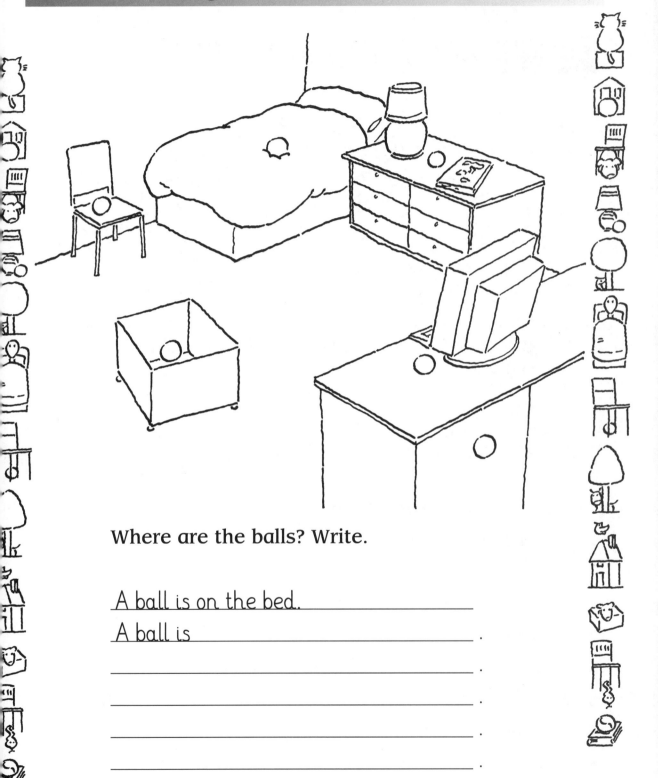

Your writing

Where are the balls? Write.

A ball is on the bed.
A ball is _____ .
_____ .
_____ .
_____ .
_____ .

Unit 6

Reading and understanding

1 Look and read.

It is a beautiful day on the beach. The sky is blue and the sea is green.
Mum and Dad are in their beach chairs. Dad has got a hat. Mum has got an umbrella.
Mikey is in the water. He says, 'I've got a big red crab.'
Pat says, 'I can see a starfish in the rock pool.'

2 Cross out the wrong answers.

1	It is a beautiful day on the	~~moon.~~	beach.
2	The sky is	green.	blue.
3	Mum and Dad are sitting in their	tables.	chairs.
4	Dad has got a	hat.	cat.
5	Mum has got an	owl.	umbrella.
6	Mikey is in the	tree.	water.
7	The crab is	red.	black.
8	Pat can see a	goldfish.	starfish.

Sentence building

My brother is (Ben).

proper noun

1 Find the proper noun. Circle the proper noun.

1 Has Ben got a hat?

2 Is Mobi on the beach?

3 Sam has got a ball.

4 Nina is under the tree.

5 Tilly is in the sea.

2 Write the names.

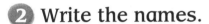

Tilly   Sam   Ben   Nina   Mobi

1 _____   2 _____   3 _____

4 _____   5 _____

3 Write your name. _____

39

Grammar

1 Write *have got* or *has got*.

1   Ben _____ a crab.

2   Look! I _____ a starfish.

3   4   She _____ two shells.

     I _____ an ice cream.

2 Colour the right answer.

1 Has he got a hat? Yes, he has. No, he hasn't.

2 Has she got a basket? Yes, she has. No, she hasn't.

3 Has she got a crab? Yes, she has. No, she hasn't.

4 Has he got a parrot? Yes, he has. No, he hasn't.

3 Write questions.

1 _____ she _____ a cat?

2 _____ he _____ a dog?

3 _____ a parrot?

4 _____ a fish?

40

Phonics

1 Choose and write.

shop shell

_____

ship shop

_____

shell ship

_____

fish dish

_____

wish dish

_____

2 Circle the *sh* words. Write the words.

q	w	r	s	h	e	l	l	t	y
z	s	h	o	p	x	c	v	b	n
m	n	b	v	s	h	i	p	z	a
p	o	k	f	i	s	h	d	f	g
y	d	i	s	h	d	r	w	q	x

shell

_____

_____

_____

_____

3 Complete the chart.

words that begin with *sh*	words that end with *sh*

Writing

Write.

crab   starfish   shell   hat   book   ice cream

1

_____

2

_____

3

_____

4

_____

5

_____

6

_____

Your writing

1 Colour the crab brown. Colour the starfish orange. Colour the shell pink. Colour the hat blue. Colour the book red. Colour the ice cream yellow.

2 Write.

1 <u>Nina has got a shell. It is pink.</u>
2 <u>Tilly has got a</u> _____ . <u>It is</u> _____
3 _____
4 _____
5 _____
6 _____

Check-up 2
Grammar

1 Write *this* or *these*. Write *It is* or *They are*.

1 What are _____ ? _____ stars.

2 What is _____ ? _____ the moon.

3 What is _____ ? _____ an owl.

4 What are _____ ? _____ trees.

2 Where is the ball? Write.

1   It is _____ the chair.

2   It is _____ the table.

3   It is _____ the car.

4   It is _____ the dolls.

3 Write *have got* or *has got*.

1 Tilly _____ a basket.

2 I _____ an umbrella.

3 _____ you _____ a pet?

4 _____ Sam _____ a parrot?

Sentence Building

1 Write the sentences correctly.

1 what is this   _____

2 what are these   _____

3 can you see the mouse   _____

2 Underline the adjectives.

1 The red mouse is in the box.   **2** I can see a blue book.

3 Underline the proper nouns.

1 Tilly has got a big shell.   **2** Can you see Sam?

Phonics

Read, match and write.

The sun is hot.   The dog can run.   The fish is on the dish.

1   _____

2      _____

3   _____

45

Move on with Mobi

1 What have they got? Draw and write.

1 ship shell

She has got a _____

2 fish frog

He has got a _____

3 fox flower

He has got a _____

4 star snake

She has got a _____

5 mug jug

She has got a _____

6 bird crab

He has got a _____

7 umbrella ice cream

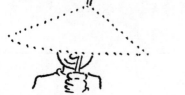

He has got an _____

8 rock box

She has got a _____

2 **Read and match.**

frog   crab   starfish   hat   apple

pool   basket   banana   wall   orange   rock

3 **Read and write.**

on   in   under   next to   between

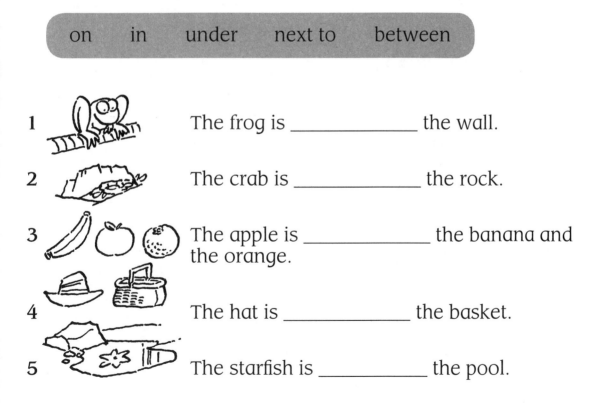

1   The frog is _____ the wall.

2   The crab is _____ the rock.

3   The apple is _____ the banana and the orange.

4   The hat is _____ the basket.

5   The starfish is _____ the pool.

Unit 7

Reading and understanding

1 Match and write.

> Good morning! Get up!   Don't stand up!   Shut the window!
> Run! Run!   Don't run!   Please sit down.

Sentence building

> **Verbs** *are doing words.*   **run**   **jump**

1 Finish the sentences. Use the verbs in the box.

look   sit   write   run

1 Tilly, _____ at the bird.

2 Ben, _____ on the bed.

3 Sam, _____ with the dog.

4 Nina, _____ your name.

2 Write the verbs. Choose a verb from the box.

Listen   Open   Shut   Read

1

_____ , Nina.

2

_____ , Tilly.

3

_____ the door, Ben.

4

_____ the window, Sam.

49

Grammar

1 **Read and tick ✔.**

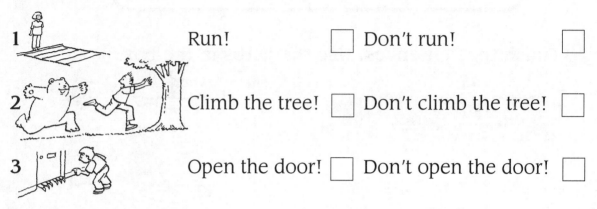

1   Run!   ☐   Don't run!   ☐

2   Climb the tree!   ☐   Don't climb the tree!   ☐

3   Open the door!   ☐   Don't open the door!   ☐

2 **Find the words.**

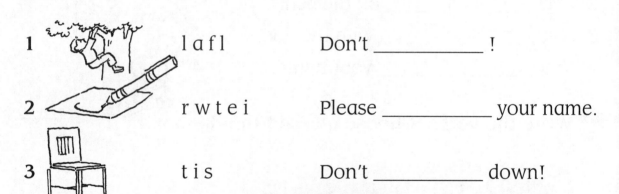

1   l a f l   Don't _____ !

2   r w t e i   Please _____ your name.

3   t i s   Don't _____ down!

3 **Write sentences.**   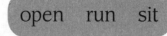 open   run   sit

1   Please _____ down.

2   Please _____ your books.

3   Don't _____ !

Phonics

1 Choose *sh* or *ch*.

1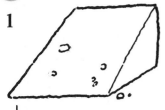

ch eese

cheese

2

___op

_____

3

fi___

_____

4

___ell

_____

5

___ips

_____

6

wat___

_____

7

___ildren

_____

8

di___

_____

9

___icken

_____

2 Complete the chart.

ch words	*sh* words

Writing

Write.

Please read!   Listen, please!   Sing!

Sit down, please!   Please open the door!   Don't run!

1

2

3

4

5

6

Your writing

Write.

1

2

3

4

5

6

Unit 8

Reading and understanding

1 Read and write.

| This owl is brown and white. It is sitting in a tree. It is very still. | This bear is white. It lives in the cold ice and snow. It is sleeping. |

| This crocodile is green. It is swimming in the river. | This tiger is black and yellow. It can run very fast. |

What is ...

a) black and yellow?   The tiger is black and yellow.

b) white?   _____

c) green?   _____

d) brown and white?   _____

2 Label the pictures.

_____   _____   _____   _____

Sentence building

> A **statement** tells us something.　Tilly is happy⊙
>
> A **question** asks us something.　Is Tilly happy?

1 Finish the sentences with a full stop or a question mark.

1　Ben is holding a ball ____

2　Is Tilly cold ____

3　Is the elephant grey ____

4　Nina is sleeping ____

2 Make these statements into questions.

1　He is swimming.

_____

2　They are playing football.

_____

3 Make these questions into statements.

1　Are the boys fishing?

_____

2　Are they singing?

_____

Grammar

1 What is Ben saying? Read and match. Write the letters.

1 ☐

2 ☐

3 ☐

a (I am swimming.)

b (I am jumping.)

c (I am swinging.)

2 Complete the sentences. Use the words in the box.

He is   She is   It is   They are

1 _____ holding an umbrella.

2 _____ playing football.

3 _____ sleeping.

4 _____ sitting under a tree.

3 Write sentences. These words can help you.

swimming   jumping   sleeping

1 _____

2 _____

3 _____

56

Phonics

1 Say the sounds. Write the words.

1

i	ll

_____

2

h	i	ll

_____

3

t	i	ll

_____

4

f	i	ll

_____

2 Write.

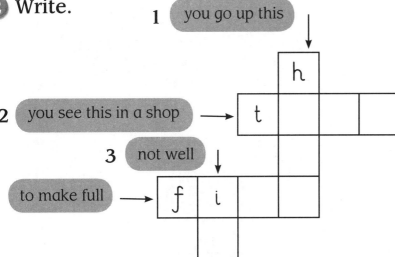

1 you go up this

2 you see this in a shop → | t | | | |

3 not well

4 to make full → | f | i | | |

3 Choose and write.

1
wall mall

_____

2
ball bell

_____

3
doll dull

_____

Writing

Write.

swimming climbing sleeping running
jumping sitting writing playing

1

2

3

_____   _____   _____

4

5

_____   _____

6

7

8

_____   _____   _____

Your writing

Write.

1 (crocodiles)

Look at the _crocodiles_ ! They are _swimming_ .

2 (tiger)

Look at the _____ It is _____

3 (Sam)

_____ He _____

4 (Tilly)

_____ She _____

5 (Sam)

_____

6 (lions)

_____

7 (Tilly)

_____

Unit 9

Reading and understanding

Choose and write.

1

garden   playground

These children are in the _____

2

dancing   marching

These boys are _____ in a line.

3

singing   skipping

These girls are _____

4

tennis   football

These boys are playing _____

5

boys   girls

These _____ are dancing in a ring.

6

climbing   hopping

These children are _____

Sentence building

She **is** running.

They **are** playing.

Is or *are*? Write.

swimming sitting climbing playing drawing sleeping

1

She _____ _____ .

2

They _____ _____ .

3

He _____ _____ .

4

They _____ _____ .

5

It _____ _____ .

6

They _____ _____ .

Grammar

1 Look, read and match.

1	Are Nina and Sam singing?	Yes, they are.	No, they aren't.
2	Is Ben climbing?	Yes, he is.	No, he isn't.
3	Is Miss Plum playing a drum?	Yes, she is.	No, she isn't.
4	Is Tilly riding a bicycle?	Yes, she is.	No, she isn't.
5	Are Sam and Ben marching?	Yes, they are.	No, they aren't.
6	Is Mobi sleeping?	Yes, he is.	No, he isn't.

2 Look and write.

> She is not   He is not   It is not   They are not

1 _____ sleeping.

2 _____ riding a bike.

3 _____ singing.

4 _____ climbing.

Phonics

1 Say the sounds. Write the words.

k ing

_____

r ing

_____

s ing

_____

w ing

_____

2 Say each word. Choose the letter.

w   s   r   k

___ing

_____

___ing

_____

___ing

_____

___ing

_____

3 Write.

1

I like my _____

2

I can _____

3

This is a _____

4

A bird has got a _____

Writing

Write.

swimming dancing marching clapping fishing jumping

1

Nina is dancing.

2

Sam

3

Tilly

4

Ben

5

Scott

6

Meg

Your writing

Write.

Nina is swimming.
Sam

Check-up 3

Grammar

1 **What are they doing? Write.**

1   The baby _____ .

2   The boys _____ into the water.

3   I _____ a book.

2 **Write the missing words.**

1   The girl _____ not _____ an elephant.

2   _____ the girl _____ a cat?

3   The children _____ not _____ drums.

3 **Find the words. Write.**

1   (pone) (thus)   Please, _____ the window and _____ the door.

2   (blimc)   Don't _____ the tree!

3   (endca) (gins)   Don't _____ and _____ in the classroom!

Sentence Building

1 **Underline the verbs.**

1 Shut the window!   **2** Please stand up.   **3** Jump on the bed.

2 **Complete the sentences with *is* or *are*.**

1 _____ he swimming?   **2** They _____ not singing.

3 Sam and Ben _____ climbing.

Phonics

1 **Find the six words.**

q	w	s	i	n	g	r	t	y	p
z	x	c	v	b	c	h	i	p	s
f	h	i	l	l	g	h	k	j	y
k	p	w	k	i	n	g	q	w	r
w	c	h	i	l	d	r	e	n	z
c	v	b	w	a	l	l	m	n	w

2 **Write the words.**

ch words	*ll* words	*ng* words

Move on with Mobi

1 What animals can you see? Tick ✔ the boxes.

chicken ☐

owl ☐

elephant ☐

tiger ☐

polar bear ☐

crocodile ☐

monkey ☐

fox ☐

snake ☐

2 Draw a trunk on the elephant.
Colour the elephant brown.

3 Draw two butterflies.
Colour one butterfly red.
Colour one butterfly yellow.

4 **Read and choose.**

1 Bob is
- eating.
- (sitting.)

2 Ned is
- kicking.
- drinking.

3 Jill is
- jumping.
- running.

4 Sam is
- running.
- reading.

5 Anna is
- kicking.
- eating.

6 Dan is
- drinking.
- jumping.

7 Pat is
- climbing.
- reading.

8 Tim is
- reading
- running.

Unit 10

Reading and understanding

Read. Number the pictures in order.

It's ten o'clock. Suki is playing with her friends.

It is time for lunch at half past twelve.

It's seven o'clock. Suki is getting up.

At three o'clock Suki is thirsty.

It's half past seven. Suki is tired. She is going to bed.

At half past five Suki is hungry.

Sentence building

> The days of the week are **proper nouns**.
> Proper nouns begin with **capital letters**.

1 **What day is it? Write.**

1 It is S _ t _ _ _ _ _. Ben is running.

2 It is S u _ _ _ _. Ben is fishing.

3 It is M _ _ _ _ _. Ben is riding.

4 It is T _ e _ _ _ _. Ben is drawing.

5 It is W _ _ n _ _ _ _ _. Ben is climbing.

6 It is T _ _ r _ _ _ _. Ben is sleeping.

7 It is F _ _ _ _ _. Ben is singing.

2 **Complete the missing words. Use words from the box.**

> **S**aturday **S**unday **M**onday **T**uesday
> **W**ednesday **T**hursday **F**riday

1 Saturday ⟶ _____ ⟶ Monday

2 Sunday ⟶ _____ ⟶ Tuesday

3 Monday ⟶ _____ ⟶ Wednesday

4 Tuesday ⟶ _____ ⟶ Thursday

Grammar

1 **Read and match. Write the letters.**

1 It is eight o'clock. ☐

2 It is half past three. ☐

3 It is half past twelve. ☐

4 It is four o'clock. ☐

5 It is eleven o'clock. ☐

6 It is half past nine. ☐

2 **What is the time? Write.**

1 It is _____ o'clock.

2 It is half past _____

3 _____

3 **Read and colour.**

1 It is the day after Monday. Colour it blue.

2 It is the day before Friday. Colour it green.

3 It is the day before Sunday. Colour it red.

4 It is the day between Tuesday and Thursday. Colour it yellow.

5 It is the day after Thursday. Colour it purple.

6 It is the day before Tuesday. Colour it orange.

7 It is the day after Saturday. Colour it pink.

72

Phonics

1 Match and write.

rock   clock   sock

1 _____

2 _____

3 _____

2 Write.

1

a __sock__ on a _____

2

a _____ on a _____

3

a _____ on a _____

4

a _____ on a _____

3 Choose and write.

1

sock   sack

_____

2

truck   trick

_____

3

duck   dock

_____

Writing

Write.

a bike   a horse   an elephant   a bus   a train   a boat

1

bu_ _s_

This is a ____bus____ .

2

b__ __ __

This is a _____

3

h__ __ __ __

This _____

4

e__ __ __ __ __ __ __ __

This _____

5

t __ __ __ __

This is a _____

6

b__ __ __

This is a _____

Your writing

Write.

1 Saturday

It is Saturday. I am riding on a _____ .

2 Sunday

It is _____ . I _____ .

3 Monday

_____

4 Tuesday

_____

5 Wednesday

_____

6 Thursday

_____

7 Friday

_____

Unit  Reading and understanding

Read and write.

> The train is going very fast. It is making a noise.
> People are sitting on the train.
> Some people are reading books.
> Some people are talking to their friends.
> Some people are listening to music.
> Some people are looking out of the window.
> Some people are eating and drinking.

1 The train is going very _fast._

2 Some people are _____ books.

3 Some people are _____ out of the window.

4 Some people are _____ to music.

5 Some people are _____ to their friends.

6 Some people are eating and _____

Sentence building

The **dog** is running.
noun

The **boys** are riding.
noun

It is running.
pronoun

They are riding.
pronoun

1 Read the sentences. Underline the pronouns.

1 He is climbing the tree.

2 What are they doing?

3 It is running.

4 Is he playing football?

5 She is riding a bike.

2 Write the correct pronoun.

He   She   It   They

1 Tilly is climbing. _____ is climbing.

2 The dogs are running. _____ are running.

3 The flower is pink. _____ is pink.

4 Dani counts the sheep. _____ counts the sheep.

5 Ben is holding a crab. _____ is holding a crab.

6 Tilly and Nina like apples. _____ like apples.

7 Dad has got a hat. _____ has got a hat.

Grammar

1 Write *I'm*, *He's*, *She's* or *They're*.

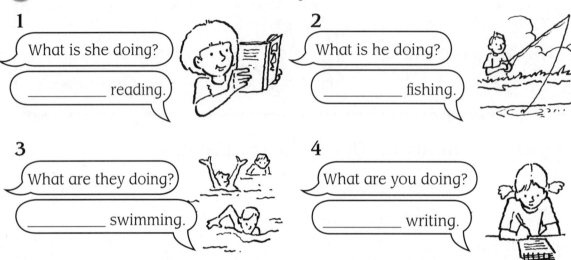

1

What is she doing?

_____ reading.

2

What is he doing?

_____ fishing.

3

What are they doing?

_____ swimming.

4

What are you doing?

_____ writing.

2 Look and write questions. Then write the answers.

1 _____   They are _____

2 _____   It is _____

3 _____   She is _____

3 What are you doing? Look and write.

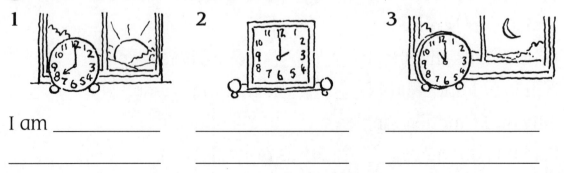

1   **2**   **3**

I am _____   _____   _____

_____   _____   _____

Phonics

1 **Write the words. Read the words you make.**

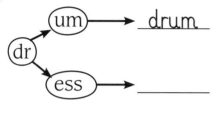

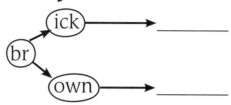

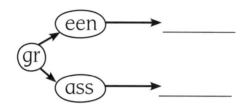

2 **Draw a girl with a red dress.** **Draw a boy with a drum.**

The girl has got a red _____   The boy has got a _____

3 **Colour the grass green.** **Colour the brick brown.**

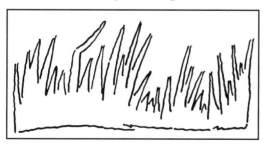

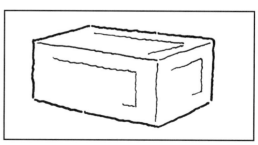

The _____ is _____   The _____ is _____

Writing

Choose the correct word.

1

eating   walking

I can see a man.

He is ___walking___ .

2

running   eating

I can see ducks.

They are _____ .

3

reading   swimming

_____ a girl.

She is _____ .

4

drinking   walking

_____ a dog.

It is _____ .

5

drinking   running

_____ a woman.

She is _____ .

6

reading   swimming

_____ a boy.

He is _____ .

Your writing

What can you see? What are they doing?

I can see ducks. They are swimming.

Unit  12

Reading and understanding

1 Look and read.

In the mall there are lots of shops.
In the cake shop there are buns and cakes and biscuits.
You can get pizzas at 'Gino's Place'.
'Happy Books' is a children's book shop.
The toy shop is quite small.
You can get trainers and boots and party shoes at the shoe shop.
At the sweet shop you can get chocolates and ice cream.

2 Write the answers. Where can you get ...

1 cakes? <u>at the cake shop</u>   2 toys? _____

3 trainers? _____   4 ice cream? _____

5 pizzas? _____   6 books? _____

3 Write the answers. What can you buy at ...

1 the cake shop? _____

2 the shoe shop? _____

3 the sweet shop? _____

Sentence building

> *A **preposition** tells us where something is.*
>
> 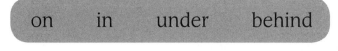 The drum is **on** the bed.

1 Complete the sentences.

on   in   under   behind

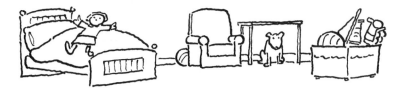

1 The dog is _____ the table.   2 The doll is _____ the bed.

3 The ball is _____ the chair.   4 The toys are _____ the box.

2 Where is it? Write.

1 Where is the doll?

_____

2 Where is the ball?

_____

3 Where is the dog?

_____

83

Grammar

1 **Read and draw.**

There is a cat on the chair. There are flowers on the table.
There is a box under the table. There are toys in the box.
There is a picture on the wall. There are two girls in the picture.

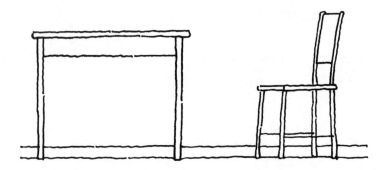

2 **Look and write.**

Look at the toy shop, the cafe and the bike shop.
What can you see?

1 <u>There are dolls</u>   in the toy shop.

2 _____ in the toy shop.

3 _____ in the toy shop.

4 _____ in the cafe.

5 _____ in the cafe.

6 _____ in the bike shop.

Phonics

1 Colour.

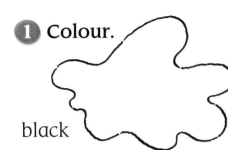

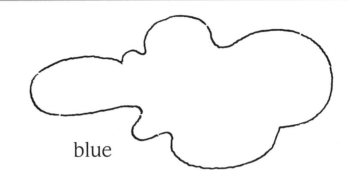

black   blue

2 Choose *cl* or *fl*.

cl ock

__clock__

__ag

_____

__own

_____

__ower

_____

3 Colour the flag black.
Colour the flower blue.

4 Colour the clown blue.
Colour the clock black.

5 Choose and write.

1 fl   pl

____ane

_____

2 bl   gl

____ass

_____

3 pl   cl

____ate

_____

Writing

Match and write.

cakes

books _____

bikes _____cakes_____

computers _____

toys _____

clothes _____

sweets _____

shoes _____

Your writing

Write the names of the shops.

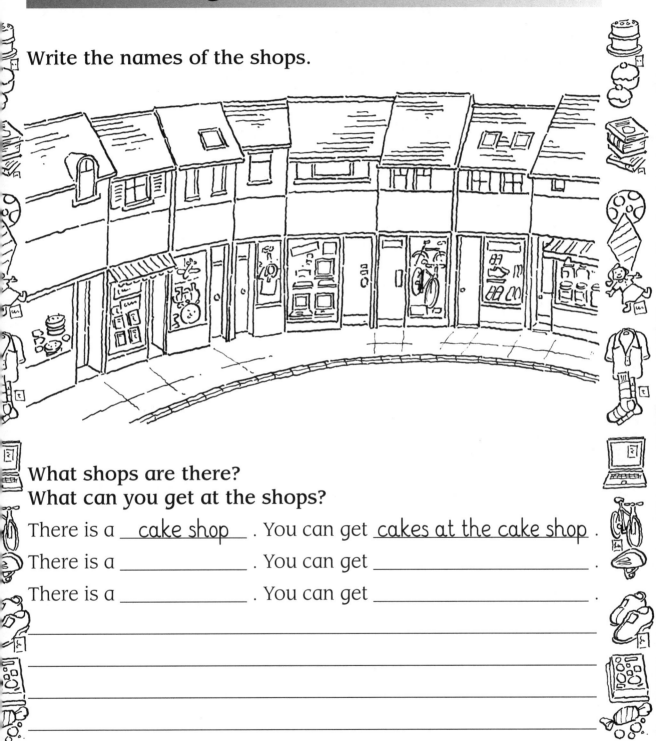

What shops are there?
What can you get at the shops?

There is a ___cake shop___ . You can get _cakes at the cake shop_ .

There is a _____ . You can get _____ .

There is a _____ . You can get _____ .

_____

_____

_____

_____

Check-up 4
Grammar

1 What is the time? Write.

1 _____

2 _____

3 _____

4 _____

2 Write the questions.

1 What _____ doing? He is riding a bike.

2 _____ ? They are running.

3 _____ ? She is dancing.

3 Write *There is* or *There are*.

1 _____ an owl in the tree.

2 _____ lots of toys in the toy shop.

3 _____ ten children in the playground.

4 _____ a castle on the hill.

Sentence Building

1 **Write the answers. What is ...**

1 he day after Wednesday? _____

2 the day before Sunday? _____

3 the day after Thursday? _____

2 **Underline the pronouns.**

1 She is riding. **2** They are playing football. **3** He is reading.

3 **Write *on* or *in*.**

1 2 3

The box is _____ the desk.

The doll is _____ the box.

The dog is _____ the bed.

Phonics

Colour the sock black.
Colour the truck brown.

Colour the dress green.
Colour the plane blue.

Move on with Mobi

1 **Read and match. Write the letters.**

1 I get up at seven o'clock. ☐
2 I go to school at eight o'clock. ☐
3 I read a book at half past nine. ☐
4 I eat my lunch at 12 o'clock. ☐
5 I swim at half past two. ☐
6 I have a drink at four o'clock. ☐
7 I watch TV at half past seven. ☐

2 **Complete the days of the week in the crossword.**

Saturday
Sunday
Monday
Tuesday
Wednesday
Thursday
Friday

3 **Trace the tracks.**

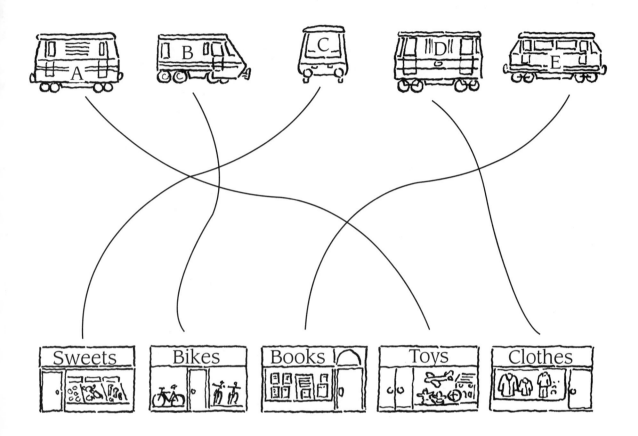

1 Train A is going to the _____ toy _____ shop.

There are __ toys __ at the ___ toy shop ___ .

2 Train B is going to the _____ shop.

There are _____ at the _____

3 Train C is going to the _____ shop.

There are _____ at the _____

4 Train D is going to the _____ shop.

There are _____ at the _____

5 Train E is going to the _____ shop.

There are _____ at the _____

Unit 13

Reading and understanding

1 Look and read.

Sami is on the hillside with his dog.
He is looking after his father's sheep.
He is with his younger brother Dani.
There are lots of sheep on the hillside.
'How many are there?' asks Dani.
'I don't know,' says Sami.
'I can count all these sheep!' Dani says.
Dani can't count all the sheep.
He is tired and sleepy.

2 Circle the correct answer.

1	Sami is on the	train	(hillside)
2	Sami has got a	dog	cat
3	Sami is looking after his father's	elephants	sheep
4	Dani is Sami's younger	brother	sister
5	Dani says he can count the	dogs	sheep
6	Dani is	tired	hungry
7	Dani is	thirsty	sleepy
8	Dani can't	eat	count

Sentence building

I **have**	we **have**
you **have**	you **have**
he **has**	they **have**
she **has**	
it **has**	

1 **Complete the sentences with *have* or *has*.**

1 He _____ got a brother.

2 I _____ got a dog.

3 You _____ got red socks.

4 She _____ got two sisters.

5 They _____ got bikes.

6 We _____ got big apples.

2 **Complete the answers.**

1 How many sheep has Sami got?

Sami _____ got three sheep.

2 How many dogs has Ben got?

Ben _____ got two dogs.

3 Have the girls got dolls?

Yes. The girls _____ got dolls.

Grammar

1 **Write the questions.**

1 How many _____ are there?

2 _____

3 _____

4 _____

5 _____

6 _____

2 **Now look at the picture and write the answers.**

1 There are _____ mountains.

2 _____ trees.

3 _____ boys.

4 _____ girl.

5 _____ stars.

6 _____ castle.

Phonics

1 Choose and write.

three   thirteen   thirty   thirty-three

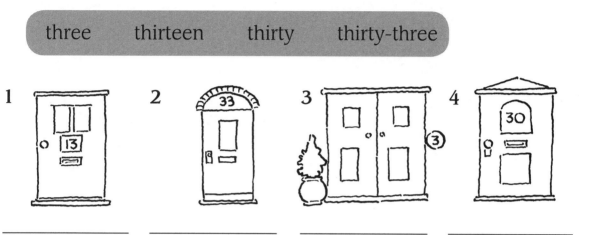

1 _____   2 _____   3 _____   4 _____

2 Choose *thick* or *thin*.

1

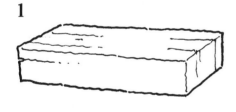

2

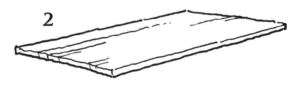

_____   _____

3 Write.

three   mouth   bath   tooth

1

I have got one _____ in my _____ .

2

I have got _____ ducks in my _____ .

95

Writing

Write.

1

How many sheep are there?
There are _____ sheep.

2

How many dogs are there?
There is _____ dog.

3

How many cows are there?

_____

4

How many horses are there?

_____

5

How many chickens are there?

_____

6

How many ducks are there?

_____

7

How many cats are there?

_____

Your writing

Count the animals on the farm. How many can you see?

On the farm there are <u>eight sheep</u> .

There are _____ .

_____ .

_____ .

There is _____ .

_____ .

Unit 14

Reading and understanding

1 Read.

'It's Monday. We're going shopping,' says Mum.
'Oh! It's windy,' says Sue.
'Look at that black cloud,' says Mum.
'I can hear thunder,' says Sue.
'Let's hurry,' says Mum.
'Oh, no! It's raining,' says Sue.
'Uh oh, there's lightning,' says Mum.
'I'm scared,' says Sue.
'Here's the supermarket,' says Mum.
'Let's go inside,' says Sue.

2 Number the sentences in order.

'Oh! It's windy,' says Sue. ☐

'Uh oh, there's lightning,' says Mum. ☐

'It's Monday. We're going shopping,' says Mum. ☐1

'Oh, no! It's raining,' says Sue. ☐

'Here's the supermarket,' says Mum. ☐

'Look at that black cloud,' says Mum. ☐

3 Write.

1 Mum and Sue are going _shopping_ .

2 Sue can hear _____   3 Sue is _____

Sentence building

> *Adjectives* tell us more about nouns.
>
> a snake   a **long** snake

1 Underline the adjectives.

1    This is a small ice cream.

2    Look at that long snake.

3    This is a big dog.

4    What is in the old box?

2 Join the opposites.

big   new

sad   little

old   happy

3 Write an adjective to go with each noun.

the _____ ball   the _____ dog   the _____ snake

Grammar

1 Read and match. Write the letters.

1 It is snowing. ☐   a

2 It is hot. ☐   b

3 It is windy. ☐   c

4 Look at the lightning! ☐   d

2 Read the questions. Circle the right answers.

1 Is it raining?   Yes, it is.   No, it isn't.

2 Is it sunny?   Yes, it is.   No, it isn't.

3 Is it cold?   Yes, it is.   No, it isn't.

4 Is it cloudy?   Yes, it is.   No, it isn't.

3 What is the weather like? Look and write.

1
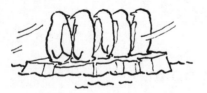

It is cold.

2

3

4

Phonics

1 Write the words. Read the words you write.

| st | ar | | sw | im | | sp | ell | | sm | ile |

_____   _____   _____   _____

2 Match the words to the pictures.

_____   _____   _____   _____

3 Write the words. Read the words you write.

| sp | ider | | st | op | | sm | ell | | sw | eet |

_____   _____   _____   _____

4 Match the words to the pictures.

_____   _____   _____   _____

5 Match the words that begin with the same letters. Write the words.

star   spell   _____   _____

swim   stop   _star_   _stop_

spider   sweet   _____   _____

Writing

1 Match and write.

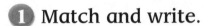

1 _____   2 _____

2 Match and write.

It is raining.   The sun is shining.   It is snowing.

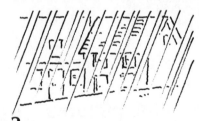

1 _____   2 _____   3 _____

3 Match and write.

It is windy.   It is foggy.   It is cloudy.

1 _____   2 _____   3 _____

Your writing

Friday Monday Saturday Sunday Thursday Tuesday Wednesday

Write about Sam's week.

Saturday   Sam is at the beach

The sun is shining

S   Sam

It

M

Tu

_____

_____

_____

Unit 15

Reading and understanding

1 Read.

A rabbit is soft and white. It has got long ears and a fluffy tail.

A duck loves to swim. It has got short legs and orange feet.

An owl has got big eyes. It flies at night.

A monkey has got long arms. It has got a long tail too.

An elephant is very big. It has got big ears and a long nose.

A giraffe eats leaves from trees. It has got long legs and a long neck.

2 Write.

1 What flies at night?   An owl.

2 What has got big ears and a long nose? _____

3 What has got long arms and a long tail?_____

4 What has got a long neck?   _____

5 What has got a fluffy tail?   _____

Sentence building

> | I **am** | we **are** |
> |---|---|
> | you **are** | you **are** |
> | he **is** | they **are** |
> | she **is** | |
> | it **is** | |

1 **Finish the sentences with** *am* **or** *is* **or** *are*.

1 She _____ kind.

2 You _____ my sister.

3 I _____ seven.

4 We _____ reading.

5 He _____ my brother.

2 **Finish the answers.**

1 Is Nina drawing?

Yes. Nina _____ drawing.

2 Is Ben sleeping?

Yes. Ben _____ sleeping.

3 Are the dogs running?

Yes. The dogs _____ running.

Grammar

1 Read and circle.

A

B

1 They have got tusks. (A)B   **2** They have got long noses.   A B

3 They have got arms.   A B   **4** They have got little ears.   A B

5 They have got trunks.   A B   **6** They have got hands.   A B

2 Write *Yes, they have.* or *No, they haven't.*

1 Have they got two eyes? _____

2 Have they got little ears? _____

3 Have they got tusks? _____

4 Have they got long noses? _____

3 Write *Yes, we have.* or *No, we haven't.*

1 Have we got tails? _____

2 Have we got trunks? _____

3 Have we got two legs? _____

4 Have we got little ears? _____

Phonics

1 Choose and write.

hand   sand   hand   band   sand   band

_____   _____   _____

2 Circle the words.

3 Colour the sink pink.

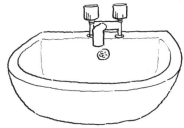

4 Circle the  in the word.

e l e p h a n t

Writing

Read. Then write the labels.

leg   head   eye   ear   tail   nose   foot   mouth

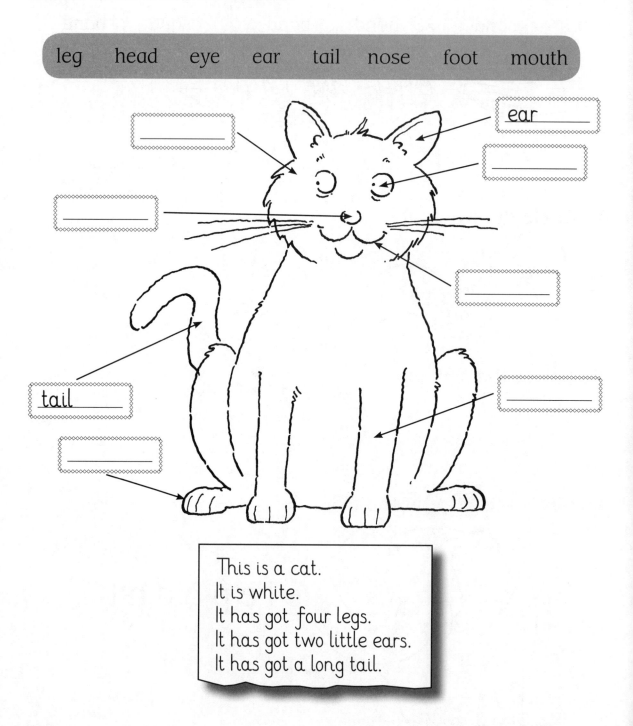

ear

tail

This is a cat.
It is white.
It has got four legs.
It has got two little ears.
It has got a long tail.

Your writing

1 Colour the dog brown and white.
What colour is its nose? Write the labels.

2 Now write about the dog.

This is a _____

It is _____

It has got _____ legs.

It has got _____

It _____

_____

Check-up 5
Grammar

1 **What is the weather like? Write.**

1 _____

2 _____

3 _____

4 _____

2 **Make questions with *How many ...?***

1 _____ There are three.

2 _____ There are two.

3 _____ There are four.

3 **Complete the sentences with *have got*.**

1 _____ you _____ a brother?

2 We _____ a nice teacher.

3 The children _____ not _____ mobile phones.

Sentence Building

1 **Write *have* or *has*.**

1 Nina _____ got a brother.   **2** The boys _____ got a dog.

3 You _____ got three apples.

2 **Underline the adjectives.**

1 It is a cloudy day.   **2** The green snake is in the grass.

3 I can see a big dog.

3 **Write *am* or *is* or *are*.**

1 The boy _____ seven.   **2** My brother _____ happy.

3 The clouds _____ black.

Phonics

Choose and write.

1	2	3
sp th ____ree	th nd mou____	sm sp ____ell
4	5	6
sm st ____ar	nk nd ha____	nd nt elepha____

Move on with Mobi

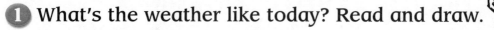

1 What's the weather like today? Read and draw.

1 Go to the beach.

It's hot and sunny.

2 It's rainy and wet.

Take an umbrella with you.

3 It is windy today.

Fly your kite.

4 Brrr! It's snowing. It's cold.

Make a snowman.

5 It's cloudy.

The sun is hiding behind a big black cloud.

2 **Read and answer the riddles.**

zebra   monkey   elephant   rabbit   crocodile   giraffe

1 I have got long arms. I eat bananas. I play in the trees. What am I? I am a _____	**2** I have got a long body. My teeth are sharp. I can swim. What am I? I am a _____
3 I am black and white. I have got four legs. I am like a horse. What am I? I am a _____	**4** I am big. I have got a long trunk. I have got a short tail. What am I? I am a _____
5 I am soft. I have got a fluffy tail. I eat carrots. What am I? I am a _____	**6** I have got a long neck. I have got four long legs. I eat leaves. What am I? I am a _____

Unit 16

Reading and understanding

1 Label the things in the picnic basket.

apples	grapes	bananas	sandwiches
pizza	biscuits	cake	sweets
chocolate	orange juice	milk	

2 Write.

1 I like to eat _____

_____

2 I like to drink _____

_____

Sentence building

> *Singular* means **one**. one book
>
> *Plural* means **more than one**. books

1 Circle the plural nouns.

> (dogs) desk apples cats
>
> tables lamp train
>
> oranges snakes rabbit ducks

2 Finish the sentences.

1 I have one _____

2 I have two _____

3 There are three _____

4 There is one _____

5 Look at the _____

6 Look at the _____

115

Grammar

Look at this!

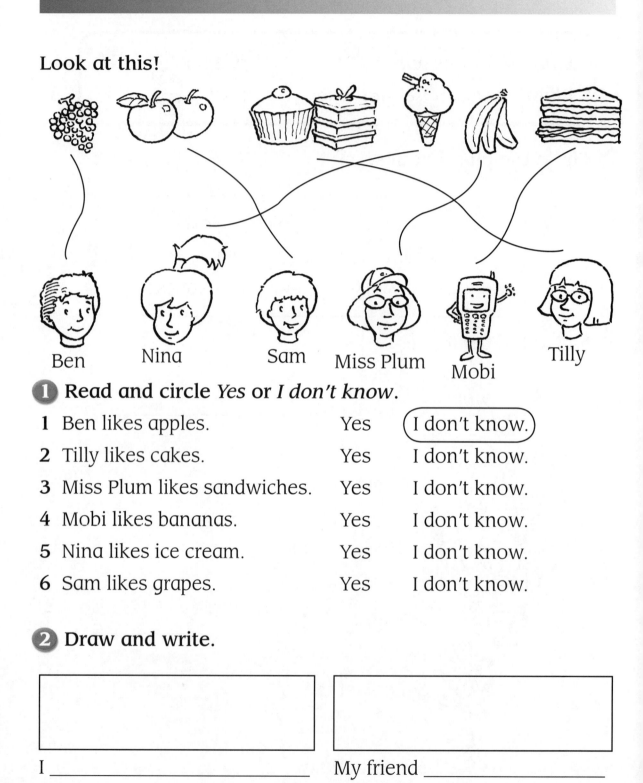

1 Read and circle *Yes* or *I don't know*.

1 Ben likes apples.	Yes	(I don't know.)
2 Tilly likes cakes.	Yes	I don't know.
3 Miss Plum likes sandwiches.	Yes	I don't know.
4 Mobi likes bananas.	Yes	I don't know.
5 Nina likes ice cream.	Yes	I don't know.
6 Sam likes grapes.	Yes	I don't know.

2 Draw and write.

I _____

My friend _____

Phonics

1 Say each word. Choose *a* or *i*.

   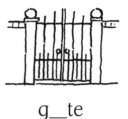

c__ke   b__ke   h__de   g__te

_____   _____   _____   _____

2 Match the rhyming words. Write the words.

make   hide   _____ _____

ride   plate   _____ _____

gate   bike   _____ _____

like   take   _____ _____

3 Write.

1 I can _____ a _____

2 I can _____ a _____

3 I can shut the _____

4 I like pizza on a _____

5 I can _____

6 I _____ books.

Writing

pears   apples   oranges   bananas   grapes   cherries

Colour and label the fruit in the shop.

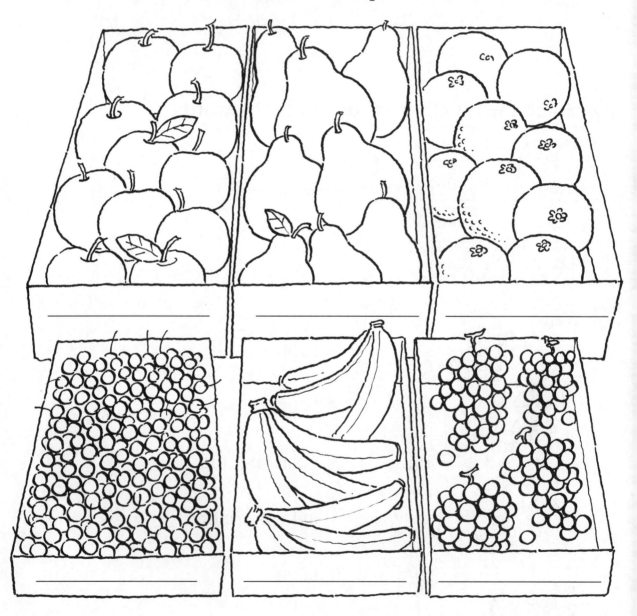

Your writing

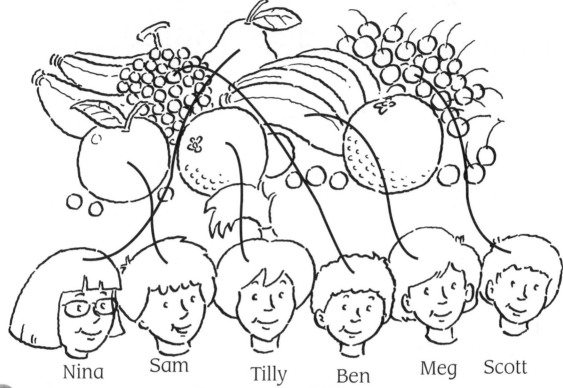

Nina   Sam   Tilly   Ben   Meg   Scott

1 **Write a sentence about each child.**

Nina likes pears.

Sam likes _____

Tilly _____

_____

_____

_____

_____

2 **Write about you.**

I like _____

I _____

I _____

119

Unit 17

Reading and understanding

1 Read. These people work at the airport.

This is Mr Black.
He is a pilot.
He is flying the plane.

This is Miss Green.
She is checking
tickets.

This is Mr Blue.
He is driving the
bus to the plane.

This is Mr Grey.
He's a cleaner.
He is cleaning windows.

This is Miss Pink.
She is making food
for the passengers.

This is Mr Red.
He is carrying
bags at the airport.

2 Who am I? Write.

1 I am cleaning windows. I am <u>Mr Grey.</u>

2 I am carrying bags. I am _____

3 I am driving the bus. I am _____

4 I am checking your tickets. I am _____

5 I am making food. I am _____

6 I am flying the plane. I am _____

Sentence building

> *The words in a **sentence** have to be in the correct order.*

Correct these sentences. The words are in the wrong order.

1 | Mr | | Grey | | cleaner. | | is | | a |

Mr Grey is a cleaner.

2 | dress | | My | | is | | green. |

_____

3 | These | | are | | socks | | Ben's. |

_____

4 | hat | | This | | is | | Tilly's. |

_____

5 | dog | | big. | | is | | The |

_____

6 | is | | name? | | your | | What |

_____

Grammar

1 Write *is this?* or *are these?*
Write the answers.

1   Whose jacket _is this_____ ?

It is _Sam's_____ .

2   Whose T-shirt _____ ?

It is _____ .

3   Whose trousers _____ ?

_____ .

4   Whose socks _____?

_____ .

5   Whose shoes _____ ?

_____ .

6   Whose trainers _____ ?

_____ .

2 Draw and write *This is my ...* or *These are my ...*

_____   _____

Phonics

1 Say each word. Choose *o* or *u*.

1

b__ne

_____

2

c__be

_____

3

n__se

_____

4

st__ne

_____

5

gl__e

_____

6

h__se

_____

7

t__be

_____

2 Match the rhyming words. Write the words.

blue   hose   _____ _____

nose   glue   _blue_ _glue_

tube   stone   _____ _____

bone   cube   _____ _____

3 Complete the chart.

words with *o* in them	words with *u* in them

Writing

Join the dots. Write the names.

cap T-shirt shorts jeans skirt shoes jumper

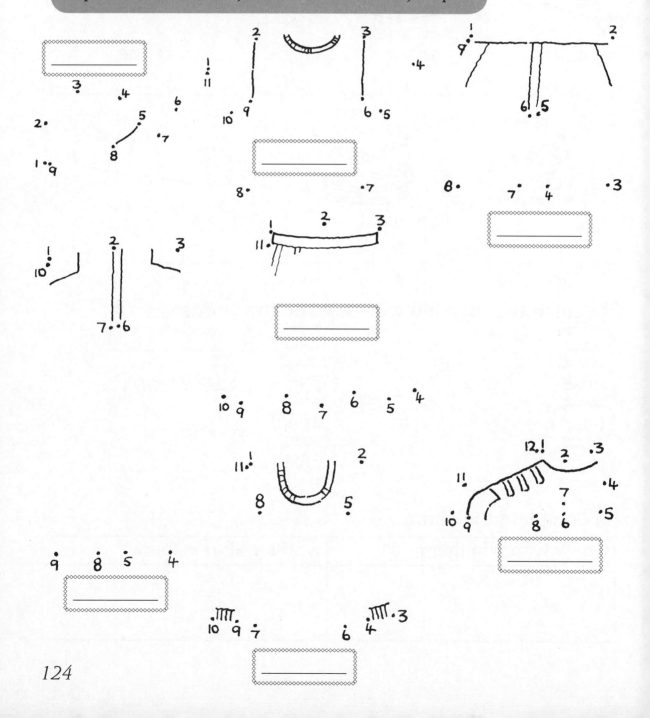

124

Your writing

1 You are going on holiday. Where are you going?
Look and circle.

forest

beach   mountains   jungle

2 What clothes are you packing?
Choose and colour your clothes.

3 Where are you going?
What have you got in your bag?
What colour are your clothes? Write.

I'm going _____

I've got _____

_____

_____

Unit 18

Reading and understanding

1 Read.

The catherine wheel goes round and round.
It makes a whizzing, whirring sound.

You can write your name in a sparkler's light
You can write it in blue and yellow, pink and white.

The waterfall is a river of light.
It fizzes and falls and lights up the night.

Look at the roman candle and see it glow
Watch the lights as they go
Ffffffffffffffffffffffffft. Ploof!

2 Write.

1 What goes round and round?

 <u>The catherine wheel goes round and round.</u>

2 What fizzes and falls and lights up the night?

 _____

3 What goes Ffffffffffffffffffffffft. Ploof!

 _____

3 What word rhymes with:

1 round? ___sound___   2 light? _____

3 night? _____   4 glow? _____

Sentence building

I like	we like
you like	you like
he likes	they like
she likes	
it likes	

1 **Complete the sentences with *like* or *likes*.**

1 She _____ red apples.

2 I _____ you.

3 He _____ computer games.

4 We _____ bees.

5 You _____ playing football.

2 **Complete the answers.**

1    Does Nina like oranges?

Yes. Nina _____ oranges.

2    Does Ben like the dog?

Yes. Ben _____ the dog.

3    Do the girls like flowers?

Yes. The girls _____ flowers.

Grammar

1 Complete the sentences. Use the words in the box.

into	onto	over	along	towards	round

1 The plane is flying ___over___ the mountains.

2 The boy is running _____ the goal.

3 The band is marching _____ the street.

4 The rabbit is jumping _____ its hole.

5 The girls are dancing _____ the fire.

6 The cat is jumping _____ the table.

2 Write sentences.

1 _____

2 _____

3 _____

4 _____

Phonics

1 **Choose and write.**

1 cold belt  _____	**2** help milk  _____	**3** old gold  _____
4 old help  _____	**5** gold cold 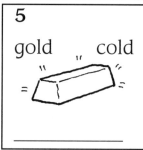 _____	**6** milk belt 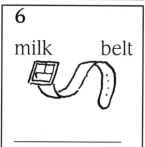 _____

2 **Write *yes* or *no*.**

1

I am old. _____

2

I like milk. _____

3

I like gold. _____

4

I am cold. _____

5

I like to help. _____

6

This is a belt. _____

Writing

onto   into   round   along   towards   over

Write.

1  The _car_ is going _along_ the _road._

2  The _____ is going _____ the _____

3  _____

4  _____

5  _____

6 _____

130

Your writing

Write the story.

1   The _____ is going _____ the _____ .

2 _____

3 _____

4 _____

5 _____

6 _____

Check-up 6
Grammar

1 Write sentences with *like* or *likes*.

1  I _____ .

2  He _____ .

2 Write the questions and the answers.

1 Whose _____ ?

_____

2 Whose _____ ?

_____

3 Complete the sentences.

1 The car is going _____ the street.

2 The car is going _____ the river _____ the forest.

3 The car is going _____ the castle.

Sentence Building

1 Underline the plural nouns.

biscuit   apples   cakes   sandwich   oranges   banana

2 Use the words to make sentences.

1 | has | | blue | | He | | shoes. |

_____

2 | at | | pink | | Look | | the | | socks! |

_____

3 | jumper | | Whose | | this? | | is |

_____

3 Write _like_ or _likes_.

She _____ dogs.   Sam _____ oranges.   I _____ cakes.

Phonics

Join up the pairs of rhyming words. Write the words.

cake — take
ride
bone   stone
cube   tube
          hide

_____ _____

_____ _____

_____ _____

_____ _____

133

Move on with Mobi

1 **Read and match.**

apples   cakes   bananas   ice cream

eggs   grapes   fish   jelly

2 **Write.**

Anna likes apples.

Ben likes b_____

Carl likes c_____

Edward likes _____

Fred likes _____

Gary likes _____

Ian likes _____

3 Read and colour.

Colour my hat red.	Colour my T-shirt orange.
Colour my coat black.	Colour my skirt pink.
Colour my trousers green.	Colour my socks red.
Colour my shoes brown.	Colour my trainers yellow.

Sam

Pam

4 Write.

1 Whose skirt is pink? <u>It is Pam's.</u>
2 Whose shoes are brown? <u>They are Sam's.</u>
3 Whose hat is red? _____
4 Whose coat is black? _____
5 Whose trousers are green? _____
6 Whose socks are red? _____
7 Whose trainers are yellow? _____
8 Whose T-shirt is orange? _____

Macmillan Education Ltd
4 Crinan Street
London N1 9XW
A division of Macmillan Publishers Limited
Companies and representatives throughout the world

ISBN 978-1-4050-1715-2

Designed by Jeffrey Tabberner
Layout by Chad Young
Illustrated by David Mostyn
Cover design by Mo Choy Design

Printed and bound in Malaysia

2017 2016 2015 2014
15 14 13 12